7/8/93

Stephanie
(An Un-birthday prezzie)

All my love
always
Your loving
Mum.

So Beautiful

My grandmother's
natural beauty creams,
lotions and remedies

*Decorated throughout
with line drawings
by the author*

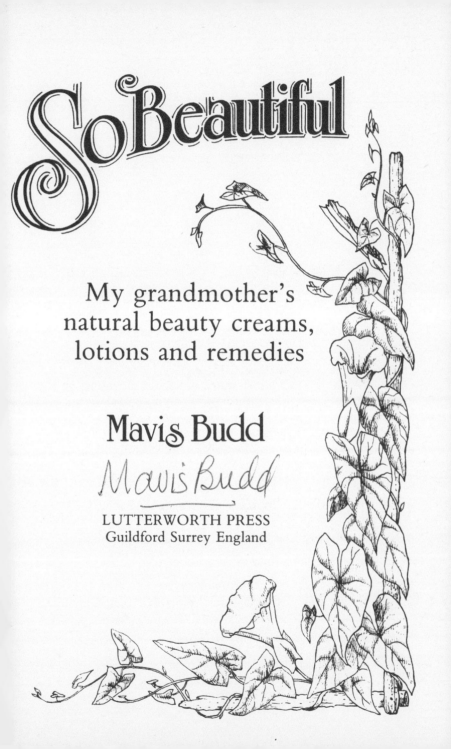

So Beautiful

My grandmother's
natural beauty creams,
lotions and remedies

Mavis Budd

Mavis Budd

LUTTERWORTH PRESS
Guildford Surrey England

First published 1981

Copyright © 1981 by Mavis Budd

ISBN 0 7188–2511–X

Phototypeset by Input Typesetting Ltd., London
SW19 8DR

Printed by
Mackays of Chatham Ltd

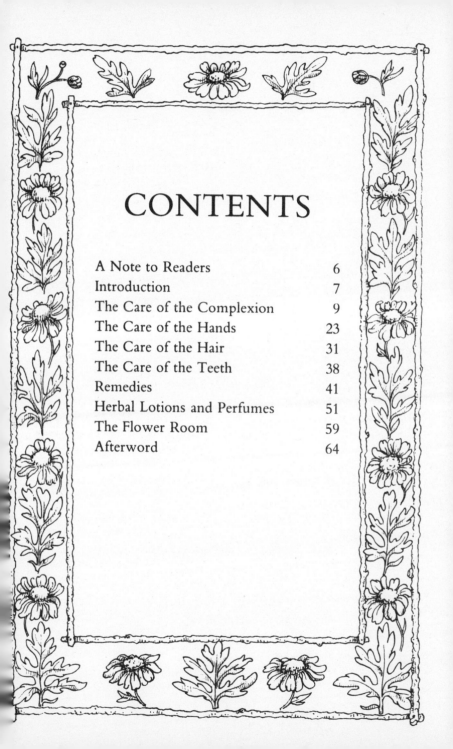

CONTENTS

A Note to Readers

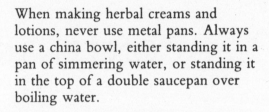

When making herbal creams and lotions, never use metal pans. Always use a china bowl, either standing it in a pan of simmering water, or standing it in the top of a double saucepan over boiling water.

Gather the herbs carefully, as described on page 53, and try to keep a good store of dried herbs, particularly those whose harvesting season is short.

My grandmother's recipes use the traditional measurements which are still familiar to many of us: ounces and pounds and pints, besides the simpler cups, spoons, handfuls and pinches. If you need to translate them into metric measurements, call an ounce 25 grammes, and a pint 600 millilitres.

An infusion is made by placing the herb, whatever it may be, in water, in a pan. Cover to avoid losing steam. Heat slowly, but do not boil. Remove the pan from the heat and leave the contents to steep . . . a few hours, or overnight. Finally, strain the liquid.

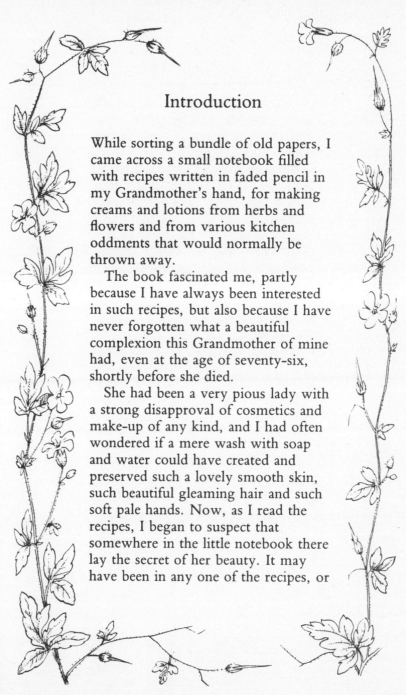

Introduction

While sorting a bundle of old papers, I came across a small notebook filled with recipes written in faded pencil in my Grandmother's hand, for making creams and lotions from herbs and flowers and from various kitchen oddments that would normally be thrown away.

The book fascinated me, partly because I have always been interested in such recipes, but also because I have never forgotten what a beautiful complexion this Grandmother of mine had, even at the age of seventy-six, shortly before she died.

She had been a very pious lady with a strong disapproval of cosmetics and make-up of any kind, and I had often wondered if a mere wash with soap and water could have created and preserved such a lovely smooth skin, such beautiful gleaming hair and such soft pale hands. Now, as I read the recipes, I began to suspect that somewhere in the little notebook there lay the secret of her beauty. It may have been in any one of the recipes, or even in several of them used regularly, or perhaps occasionally, but of one thing I feel certain. She must have used them all at some time.

The notebook included numerous remedies for the treatment and relief of various minor ills, and these interested me too, for my Grandmother had always refused to take drugs of any kind. I had often wondered how she soothed her headaches and dealt with warts and bee stings, fatigue and hiccoughs. Now I knew, and I was just as fascinated by the hints as I was by the recipes.

And this is the collection. I have done a little editing where necessary, but in general it is copied word for word as she first wrote it. Everything is so easy to make, so beautiful to use, and so full of promise.

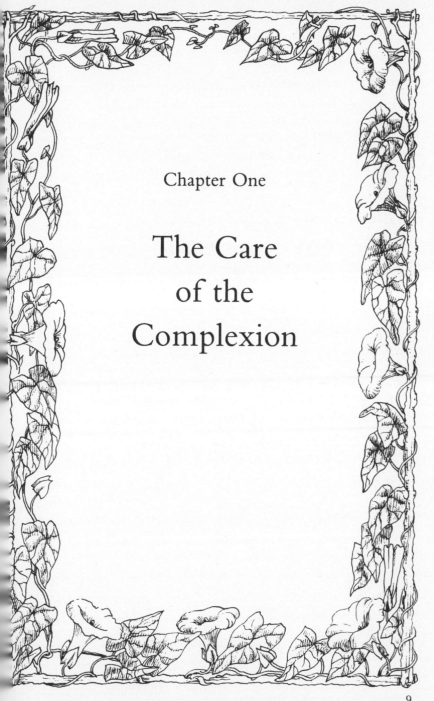

Chapter One

The Care
of the
Complexion

Take ye pint glass and fill it with elderflowers pickt clean from ye stem. Pour in some of ye best meat oyle and fill ye glass and lett it stand against a sunny window for a fortnight and so keep it for use. Ye flowers must not be strained off. Tis good for a strain or ache or bruise.

A recipe for elderflower cream used in the thirteenth century. To try it, substitute olive oil for best meat oyle.

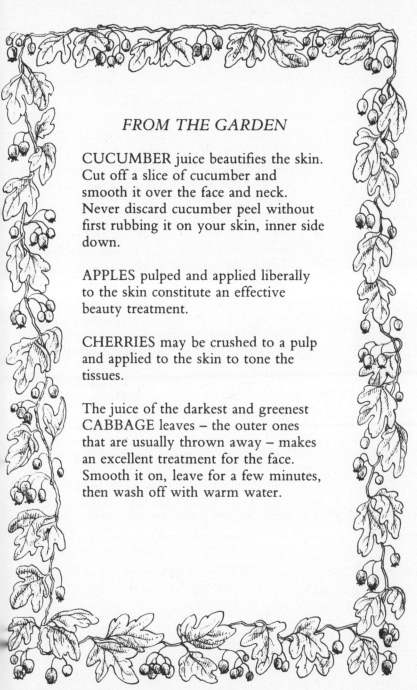

FROM THE GARDEN

CUCUMBER juice beautifies the skin.
Cut off a slice of cucumber and
smooth it over the face and neck.
Never discard cucumber peel without
first rubbing it on your skin, inner side
down.

APPLES pulped and applied liberally
to the skin constitute an effective
beauty treatment.

CHERRIES may be crushed to a pulp
and applied to the skin to tone the
tissues.

The juice of the darkest and greenest
CABBAGE leaves – the outer ones
that are usually thrown away – makes
an excellent treatment for the face.
Smooth it on, leave for a few minutes,
then wash off with warm water.

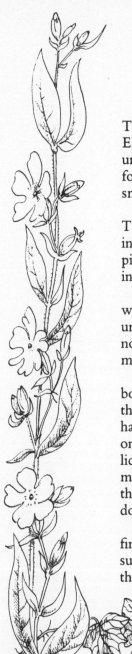

ELDERFLOWERS

To make a CREAM OF
ELDERFLOWERS which is
unfailingly good for the complexion
for it renders the skin very white and
smooth.

Take a jar of cold cream and empty it
into a china bowl. Add as many freshly
picked elderflowers as you can press
into the cream.

Stand the bowl in a pan of boiling
water and let it simmer very gently
until the cream is liquid and warm but
not hot. This will take about twenty
minutes.

Remove from the heat. Cover the
bowl and leave the petals to steep until
the following day when the cream will
have set. Warm the bowl in hot water
once again and when the cream is
liquid, strain it through very fine
muslin and pour into jars. As soon as
the liquid has cooled screw the jars
down very tightly.

Leave in a cold place to harden. The
finished cream will be a delicate green,
subtly scented with elderflowers and
the lingering breath of butterflies.

TO SOOTHE AND BEAUTIFY

To make AN ELDERFLOWER
OINTMENT that will soothe sunburn
and windburn, repeat the process for
making the beauty cream but use pure
vaseline instead of cold cream. This
ointment will soothe the worst ravages
of the elements.

FOR A QUICKLY MADE BEAUTY
CREAM, pound to a pulp with a
wooden spoon whatever herb you
decide to use. Stir the pulp into cold
cream and apply to the face and neck.
Rinse off with lukewarm water.

FOR A SIMPLE LOTION use equal
parts of rosewater and glycerine mixed
with the unbeaten white of an egg.
Smooth on the face. Leave to dry, then
rinse off with warm water.

FOR WATERCRESS LOTION mix
well together two parts of well-crushed
watercress and one part of honey.
Strain through a fine cloth. Dab on the
face with cotton wool night and
morning. Massage well, then rinse off
with lukewarm water.

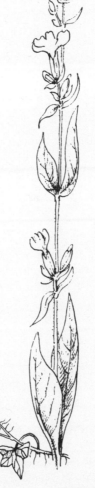

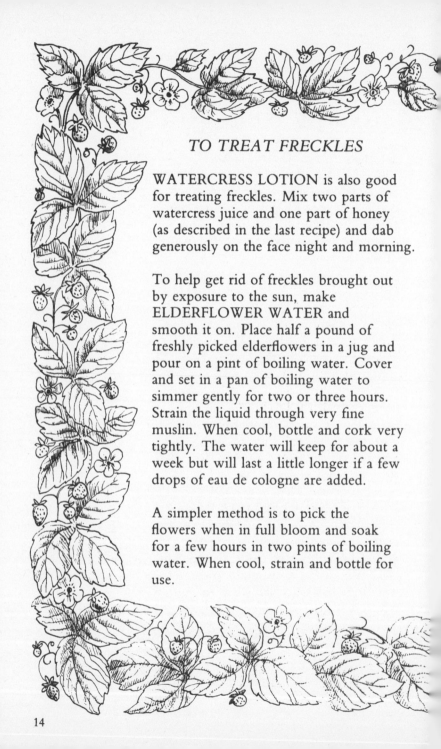

TO TREAT FRECKLES

WATERCRESS LOTION is also good
for treating freckles. Mix two parts of
watercress juice and one part of honey
(as described in the last recipe) and dab
generously on the face night and morning.

To help get rid of freckles brought out
by exposure to the sun, make
ELDERFLOWER WATER and
smooth it on. Place half a pound of
freshly picked elderflowers in a jug and
pour on a pint of boiling water. Cover
and set in a pan of boiling water to
simmer gently for two or three hours.
Strain the liquid through very fine
muslin. When cool, bottle and cork very
tightly. The water will keep for about a
week but will last a little longer if a few
drops of eau de cologne are added.

A simpler method is to pick the
flowers when in full bloom and soak
for a few hours in two pints of boiling
water. When cool, strain and bottle for
use.

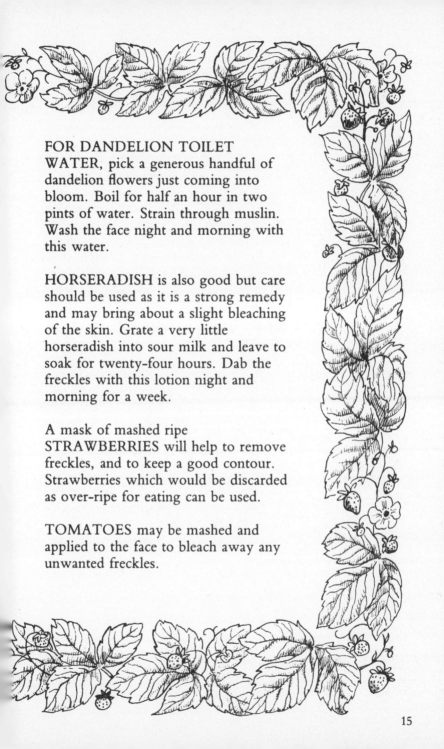

FOR DANDELION TOILET
WATER, pick a generous handful of
dandelion flowers just coming into
bloom. Boil for half an hour in two
pints of water. Strain through muslin.
Wash the face night and morning with
this water.

HORSERADISH is also good but care
should be used as it is a strong remedy
and may bring about a slight bleaching
of the skin. Grate a very little
horseradish into sour milk and leave to
soak for twenty-four hours. Dab the
freckles with this lotion night and
morning for a week.

A mask of mashed ripe
STRAWBERRIES will help to remove
freckles, and to keep a good contour.
Strawberries which would be discarded
as over-ripe for eating can be used.

TOMATOES may be mashed and
applied to the face to bleach away any
unwanted freckles.

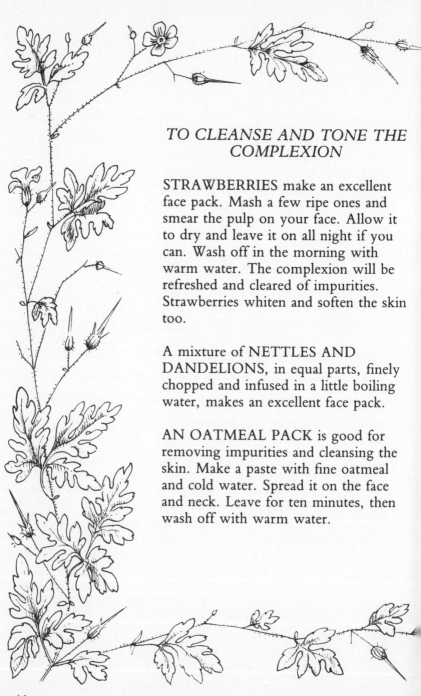

TO CLEANSE AND TONE THE COMPLEXION

STRAWBERRIES make an excellent face pack. Mash a few ripe ones and smear the pulp on your face. Allow it to dry and leave it on all night if you can. Wash off in the morning with warm water. The complexion will be refreshed and cleared of impurities. Strawberries whiten and soften the skin too.

A mixture of NETTLES AND DANDELIONS, in equal parts, finely chopped and infused in a little boiling water, makes an excellent face pack.

AN OATMEAL PACK is good for removing impurities and cleansing the skin. Make a paste with fine oatmeal and cold water. Spread it on the face and neck. Leave for ten minutes, then wash off with warm water.

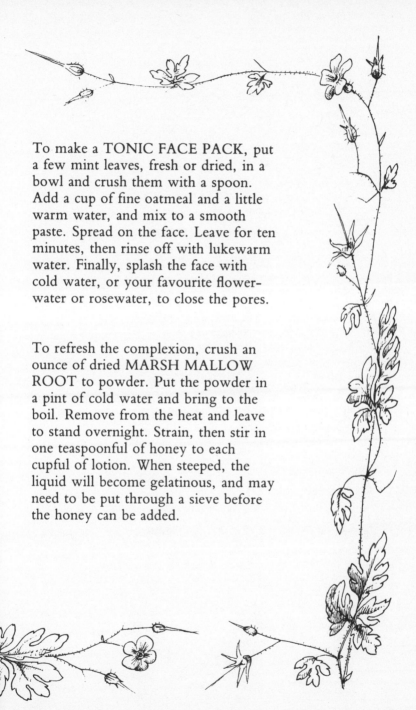

To make a TONIC FACE PACK, put
a few mint leaves, fresh or dried, in a
bowl and crush them with a spoon.
Add a cup of fine oatmeal and a little
warm water, and mix to a smooth
paste. Spread on the face. Leave for ten
minutes, then rinse off with lukewarm
water. Finally, splash the face with
cold water, or your favourite flower-
water or rosewater, to close the pores.

To refresh the complexion, crush an
ounce of dried MARSH MALLOW
ROOT to powder. Put the powder in
a pint of cold water and bring to the
boil. Remove from the heat and leave
to stand overnight. Strain, then stir in
one teaspoonful of honey to each
cupful of lotion. When steeped, the
liquid will become gelatinous, and may
need to be put through a sieve before
the honey can be added.

TO HELP IN PREVENTING WRINKLES

Make a lotion by mixing equal quantities of CUCUMBER JUICE and glycerine. Apply to the face and neck with cotton wool. Leave to dry, then rinse off with warm water.

Mix three tablespoonfuls of ELDERFLOWER WATER to one of cucumber juice. Dab on the face and neck with cotton wool, night and morning.

Smooth a raw POTATO cut in half over the face and neck.

Grate a raw POTATO and mix with a teaspoonful of cream. Pound to a smooth pulp and apply to the face and neck. Leave on for ten minutes, then wash off with warm water.

For A GOOD ANTI-WRINKLE LOTION mix together half an ounce glycerine, half an ounce rosewater, half an ounce witch hazel, three tablespoonfuls honey, and smooth on.

TO COMBAT WRINKLES

An infusion of a handful of POPPY
LEAVES AND FLOWERS in two
pints of water will combat wrinkles.

A mash of RAW CARROTS including
the peel, mixed to a paste with a little
lemon juice and applied to the face, is
also good. Leave on for half an hour,
then rinse off.

RAW BEETROOT minced very
finely, mixed to a smooth paste with a
little cream, and applied as a mask, will
work wonders.

Paint wrinkles with the lightly beaten
WHITE OF AN EGG, using a soft
brush. Leave on for ten minutes, then
wash off with warm water. Do this
once a week without fail.

Always make use of the white that
remains in the shells of the eggs you
have used for cooking. There is far
more in them than you would believe.
And smooth some on your hands, too.

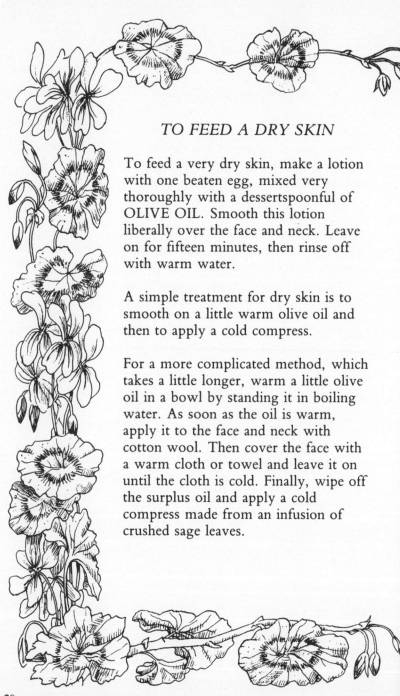

TO FEED A DRY SKIN

To feed a very dry skin, make a lotion with one beaten egg, mixed very thoroughly with a dessertspoonful of OLIVE OIL. Smooth this lotion liberally over the face and neck. Leave on for fifteen minutes, then rinse off with warm water.

A simple treatment for dry skin is to smooth on a little warm olive oil and then to apply a cold compress.

For a more complicated method, which takes a little longer, warm a little olive oil in a bowl by standing it in boiling water. As soon as the oil is warm, apply it to the face and neck with cotton wool. Then cover the face with a warm cloth or towel and leave it on until the cloth is cold. Finally, wipe off the surplus oil and apply a cold compress made from an infusion of crushed sage leaves.

TO TREAT AN OILY SKIN

Make a mask of CUCUMBER. This is slightly astringent. Cut up half a small cucumber, including the skin, and pound it smooth. Add the white of a large egg and two tablespoons of milk. Beat very well until the mixture forms a paste. Spread over the face. Leave for half an hour, then rinse off with warm water.

LEMON JUICE is helpful in treating an oily skin. Apply a little with cotton wool before washing the face.

TO TREAT LARGE PORES

An infusion of SAGE LEAVES is a
good treatment for large pores.
Smooth it on with cotton wool
regularly night and morning.

TO TREAT REDNESS OF THE FACE

Massage the face with the juice of a
white lily bulb in gentle, circular
movements.

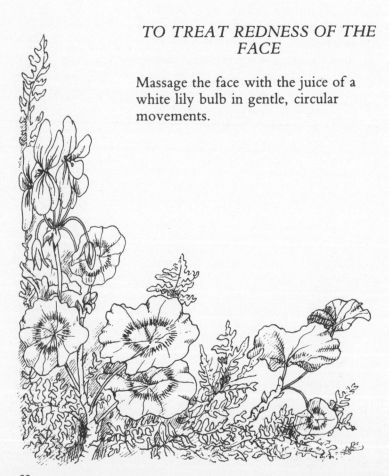

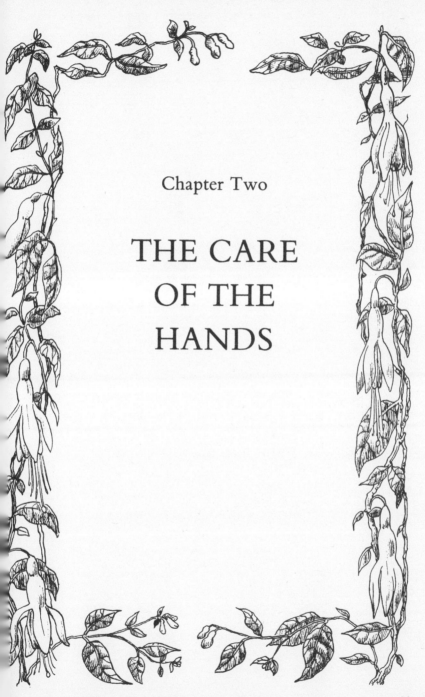

Chapter Two

THE CARE
OF THE
HANDS

A LADY'S REMEDY FOR CHOPPED HANDS WHICH WILL PRESERVE THEM SMOOTH BY CONSTANT USE

Mix a quarter of a pound of unsalted hog's lard which has been washed in common and then in rose water, with the yolks of two new-laid eggs, and a large spoonful of honey. Add as much fine oatmeal as will work into a paste.

TO CLEANSE THE HANDS

To cleanse work-worn hands, soap them thoroughly, then rub them well with WOOD ASH.

To remove stains from the hands, rub them with a paste composed of OLIVE OIL AND SUGAR.

To keep the hands soft after washing rub them with a little SUGAR while they are still damp.

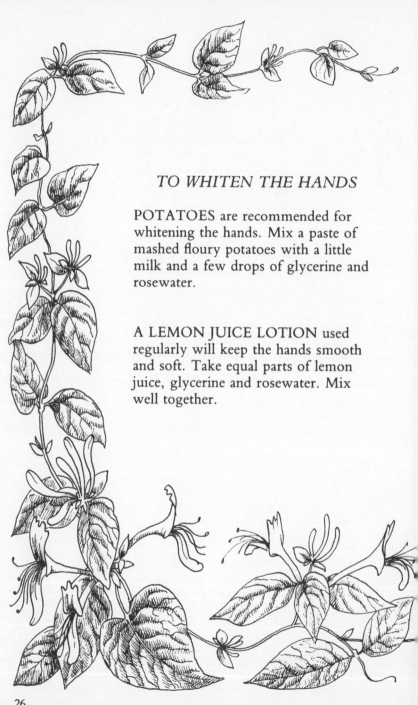

TO WHITEN THE HANDS

POTATOES are recommended for whitening the hands. Mix a paste of mashed floury potatoes with a little milk and a few drops of glycerine and rosewater.

A LEMON JUICE LOTION used regularly will keep the hands smooth and soft. Take equal parts of lemon juice, glycerine and rosewater. Mix well together.

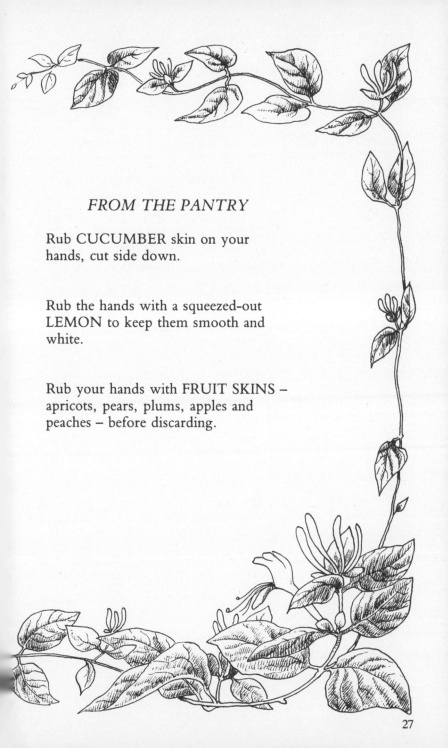

FROM THE PANTRY

Rub CUCUMBER skin on your
hands, cut side down.

Rub the hands with a squeezed-out
LEMON to keep them smooth and
white.

Rub your hands with FRUIT SKINS –
apricots, pears, plums, apples and
peaches – before discarding.

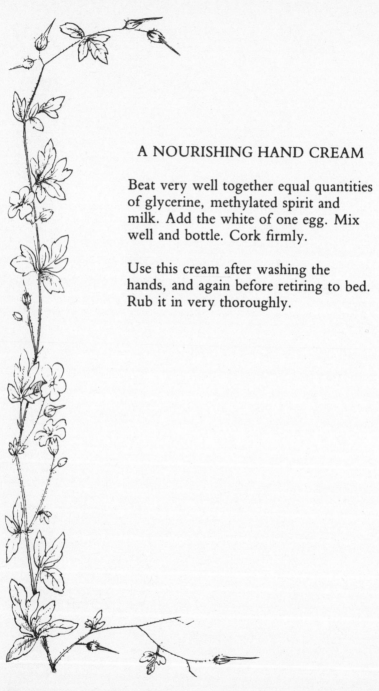

A NOURISHING HAND CREAM

Beat very well together equal quantities
of glycerine, methylated spirit and
milk. Add the white of one egg. Mix
well and bottle. Cork firmly.

Use this cream after washing the
hands, and again before retiring to bed.
Rub it in very thoroughly.

TO SOFTEN THE HANDS

A softening lotion for the hands can be made by steeping squeezed-out lemons in half a teacup of boiling water. When cool, pour off and strain. Add an ounce of powdered borax. Stir in two ounces of glycerine. Mix well. Pour into bottles and cork tightly. Use regularly.

TO TREAT CHAPPED HANDS

Soak chapped hands in an infusion made with GROUNDSEL.

TO CARE FOR THE NAILS

HORSETAIL is an excellent remedy for the nails. Make a strong infusion and soak the fingertips in the liquid as a remedy against brittle and splitting nails.

LEMON JUICE is good for the nails as well as the skin. To prevent nails splitting, rub them with lemon juice night and morning.

To strengthen the nails, massage them regularly with a little GLYCERINE.

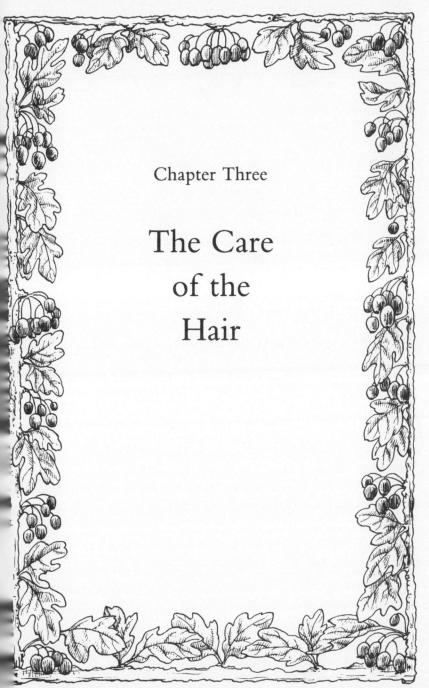

Chapter Three

The Care
of the
Hair

AN EXCELLENT WATER TO PREVENT HAIR FROM FALLING OFF AND TO THICKEN IT

Put four pounds of unadulterated honey into a still with twelve handfuls of the tendrils of vines and the same quantity of rosemary-tops. Distil as cool and as slowly as possible. The liquor may be allowed to drop until it begins to taste sour.

Advice from *A New System of Domestic Cookery formed upon Principles of Economy*, by A Lady (1837)

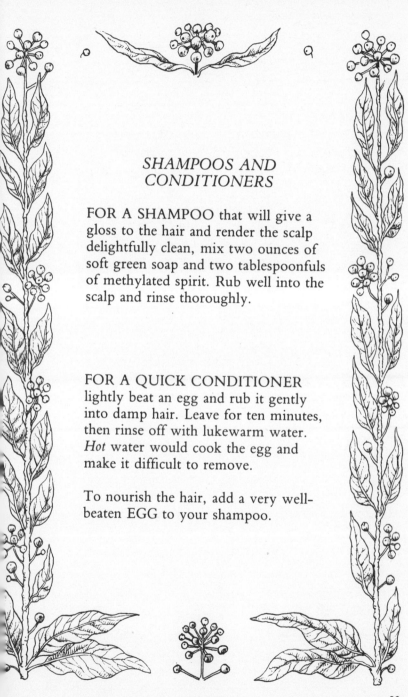

SHAMPOOS AND CONDITIONERS

FOR A SHAMPOO that will give a gloss to the hair and render the scalp delightfully clean, mix two ounces of soft green soap and two tablespoonfuls of methylated spirit. Rub well into the scalp and rinse thoroughly.

FOR A QUICK CONDITIONER lightly beat an egg and rub it gently into damp hair. Leave for ten minutes, then rinse off with lukewarm water. *Hot* water would cook the egg and make it difficult to remove.

To nourish the hair, add a very well-beaten EGG to your shampoo.

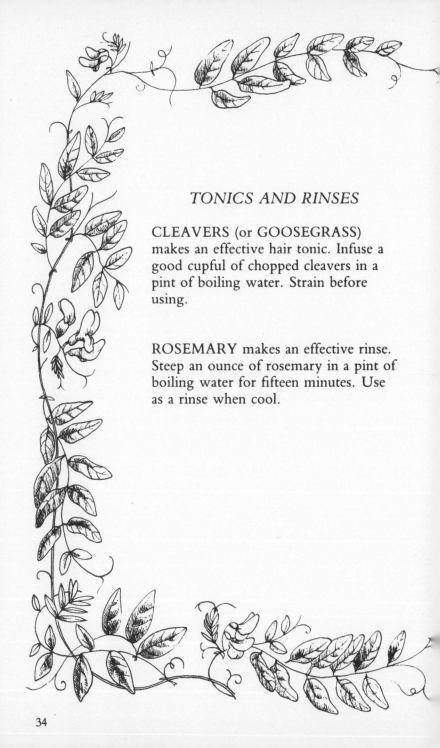

TONICS AND RINSES

CLEAVERS (or GOOSEGRASS) makes an effective hair tonic. Infuse a good cupful of chopped cleavers in a pint of boiling water. Strain before using.

ROSEMARY makes an effective rinse. Steep an ounce of rosemary in a pint of boiling water for fifteen minutes. Use as a rinse when cool.

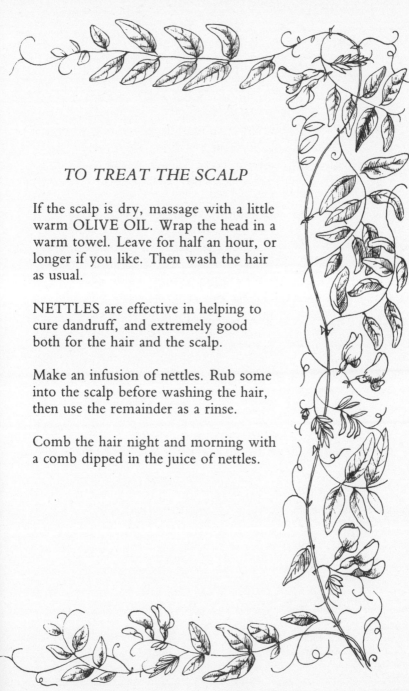

TO TREAT THE SCALP

If the scalp is dry, massage with a little warm OLIVE OIL. Wrap the head in a warm towel. Leave for half an hour, or longer if you like. Then wash the hair as usual.

NETTLES are effective in helping to cure dandruff, and extremely good both for the hair and the scalp.

Make an infusion of nettles. Rub some into the scalp before washing the hair, then use the remainder as a rinse.

Comb the hair night and morning with a comb dipped in the juice of nettles.

TO TREAT BALDNESS

To cure baldness, rub the head night
and morning with an ONION. Keep
rubbing until the skin is red, then
massage the area with honey.

For another cure, which will help to
restore the hair if the roots are not
gone, mix ten parts of cod-liver oil,
ten parts of onion juice, and five parts
either of egg white or of an egg yolk.
Beat the ingredients thoroughly and
apply to the scalp once a week.

TO CLEAN BRUSHES AND
COMBS

Wash brushes and combs in two pints
of water to which two teaspoonfuls of
AMMONIA have been added. All
grease and dirt will disappear. Rinse
well. Shake, and dry in the sun or by
the fire.

TO DARKEN THE HAIR

SAGE will darken the hair. Boil an ounce of sage leaves in two pints of water for half an hour. The red variety is best but the more usual garden sage will do admirably. Use as a rinse. The longer the sage is boiled, the darker the rinse will be.

VINEGAR will bring out the highlights in the hair. Add a good dessertspoonful to the rinsing water.

TO LIGHTEN THE HAIR

CHAMOMILE will bring out the highlights in fair hair. Boil two ounces of chamomile flowers in a pint of water for ten to fifteen minutes. Strain and use as a rinse after shampooing.

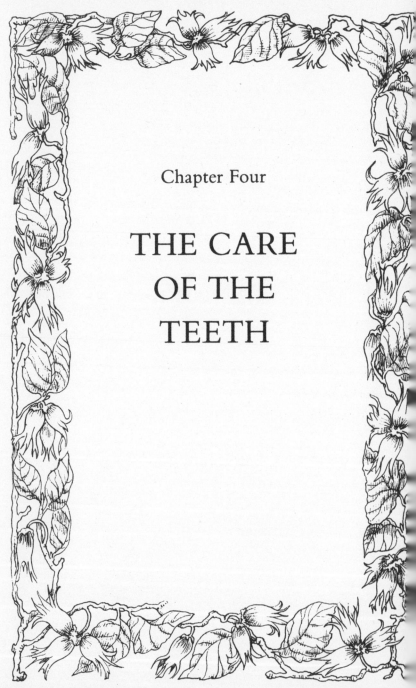

Chapter Four

THE CARE
OF THE
TEETH

TO CLEAN THE TEETH

SAGE is very good for the teeth. Rub
them each day with a sage leaf.

For a good dentifrice, bake sage leaves
in the oven till dry and brittle, then
pound to powder and add a little salt.

The juice of STRAWBERRIES will
remove tartar from the teeth.

Wash the teeth after each meal with a
mouthwash made of tepid water to
which a few drops of MYRRH have
been added.

TO TREAT THE TEETH

Massage the gums with a sliver of
LEMON PEEL to strengthen them.

Chewing fresh PARSLEY will help to
fasten teeth that are loose.

For a good GARGLE, make an
infusion of sage leaves, mix with
honey and add a pinch of cayenne
pepper.

To ease a TOOTHACHE, chew
cloves or lay hot turnip parings behind
the ear.

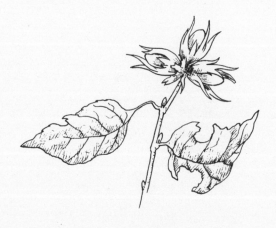

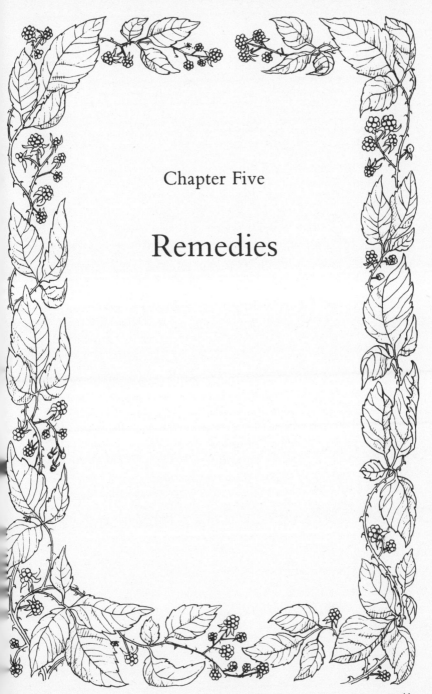

Chapter Five

Remedies

TO CHEER A SAD HEART, drink a tisane made of the petals of roses, violets, and anchusa, in equal parts. Gather quantities of the flowers when in season. Dry carefully in borax; store in screw-topped jars. When you feel dispirited, make a cup of tisane by pouring a cupful of boiling water over three tablespoonfuls of the mixed petals. Allow to infuse for about five minutes, then add a squeeze of lemon and a little honey to sweeten, if preferred. Drink the tisane slowly and your spirits will lift.

TO BANISH MELANCHOLY, drink a tisane made of the leaves of archangel. This little plant grows plentifully in shady woods and on weedy banks, blooms during the spring, and can easily be identified because it smells like weasels. Make a tisane of the leaves, either fresh or dried. Sip it, and your melancholy will fade away.

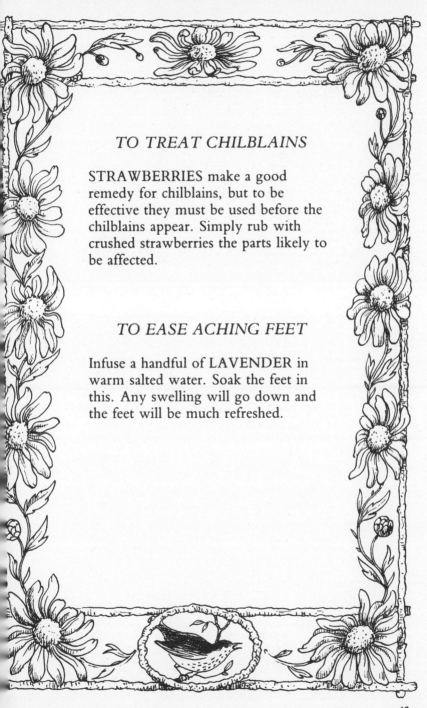

TO TREAT CHILBLAINS

STRAWBERRIES make a good
remedy for chilblains, but to be
effective they must be used before the
chilblains appear. Simply rub with
crushed strawberries the parts likely to
be affected.

TO EASE ACHING FEET

Infuse a handful of LAVENDER in
warm salted water. Soak the feet in
this. Any swelling will go down and
the feet will be much refreshed.

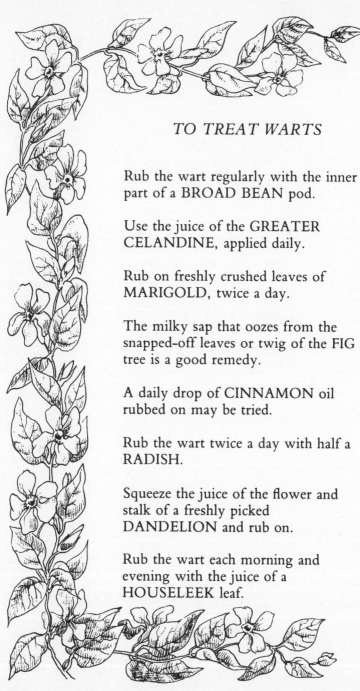

TO TREAT WARTS

Rub the wart regularly with the inner part of a BROAD BEAN pod.

Use the juice of the GREATER CELANDINE, applied daily.

Rub on freshly crushed leaves of MARIGOLD, twice a day.

The milky sap that oozes from the snapped-off leaves or twig of the FIG tree is a good remedy.

A daily drop of CINNAMON oil rubbed on may be tried.

Rub the wart twice a day with half a RADISH.

Squeeze the juice of the flower and stalk of a freshly picked DANDELION and rub on.

Rub the wart each morning and evening with the juice of a HOUSELEEK leaf.

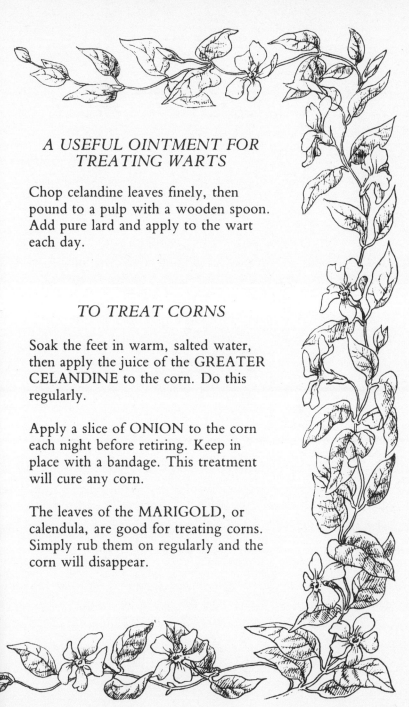

A USEFUL OINTMENT FOR
TREATING WARTS

Chop celandine leaves finely, then
pound to a pulp with a wooden spoon.
Add pure lard and apply to the wart
each day.

TO TREAT CORNS

Soak the feet in warm, salted water,
then apply the juice of the GREATER
CELANDINE to the corn. Do this
regularly.

Apply a slice of ONION to the corn
each night before retiring. Keep in
place with a bandage. This treatment
will cure any corn.

The leaves of the MARIGOLD, or
calendula, are good for treating corns.
Simply rub them on regularly and the
corn will disappear.

TO TREAT FLABBINESS

Chop a good handful of IVY leaves very finely until the sap in them creates a mash. Apply directly to the affected area.

Another treatment is to take a good handful of IVY leaves. Chop finely and boil in a little water for ten to fifteen minutes, taking care not to let the mixture boil dry. Use as a compress on the puffy areas.

TO RELIEVE INDIGESTION

Mix the juice of a LEMON with a dessertspoonful of bicarbonate of soda. Stir into a glass of water and drink slowly.

TO CHECK HICCOUGHS

Say 'Welcome, stranger' over and over again, until the hiccoughs cease.

TO TREAT SPOTS AND PIMPLES

An infusion of young BRAMBLE AND NETTLE leaves in equal quantities boiled down to a green medicine makes an excellent purifying physic for clearing spots and pimples. Take a teaspoonful in water, or mixed with honey, every day for a week.

A GOOD HEALTH DRINK which will improve the skin: take equal quantities of watercress, dandelion and borage. Steep in a little boiling water, then force through a fine sieve and bottle. Take one teaspoonful night and morning. Make a fresh supply every two or three days.

AN EFFECTIVE DEODORANT

An infusion of CLEAVERS (or GOOSEGRASS) is an effective underarm lotion, helpful in neutralising acid perspiration.

TO EASE BURNS AND STINGS

An ONION crushed with a little salt, applied to a steam burn, takes the pain away and prevents a blister forming.

A scraped POTATO is an effective remedy for a steam burn provided it is used before a blister forms.

An infusion of SAGE makes an excellent cold compress for burns.

Rub wasp and bee stings with half an ONION, or with CRUSHED PLANTAIN leaves.

Soak BLACKCURRANT leaves in white wine and apply the liquid to the sting with cotton wool.

Rub nettle stings with a PLANTAIN leaf, or with a DOCK leaf which will relieve the pain and inflammation.

TO REPEL INSECTS

To discourage gnats and midges and other stinging insects, infuse a good handful of FEVERFEW leaves in very hot water. Apply liberally to parts likely to be affected.

Crush a good handful of ELDER leaves (add the flowers too, if you like) and stew gently in a little water. Strain and bottle. Dab on as necessary.

Soak a few QUASSIA chips in cold water for twenty-four hours and apply the liquid.

Flies dislike MIGNONETTE. Put a bunch in a jar where flies are troublesome.

Sprinkle EPSOM SALTS in drawers and cupboards to discourage moths.

A few MINT leaves strewn in drawers and cupboards will help to repel insects and mice. They will also impart a pleasant and subtle perfume.

TO RELIEVE HEADACHE AND FATIGUE

Smooth a slice of CUCUMBER on the forehead and the back of the neck to relieve a tension headache.

A warmed CABBAGE leaf applied to the head and neck will relieve headache.

Throw a handful of CHAMOMILE flowers into the bath, to relieve fatigue.

TO CALM HYSTERIA

A drink of MINT TEA on going to bed has a calming effect, and an infusion of LAVENDER flowers is soothing.

TO CLEAR BAD SMELLS

Burn dry COFFEE GROUNDS in a metal shovel for a few minutes. A few leaves of dried THYME, or a sprig of dried ROSEMARY, are also pleasantly fragrant.

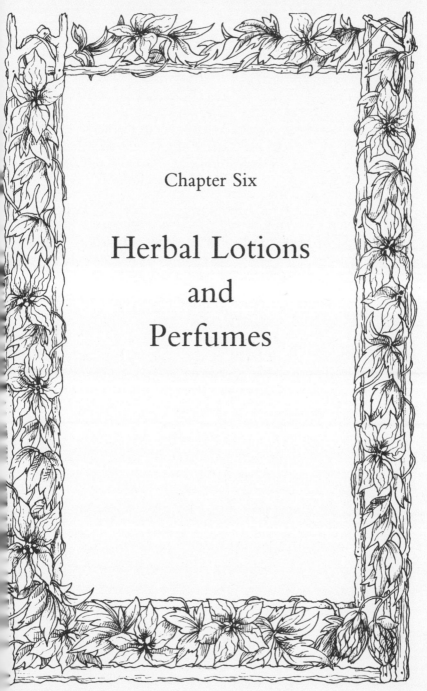

Chapter Six

Herbal Lotions
and
Perfumes

TO MAKE A SCENTED NECKLACE THAT WILL CONTINUE TO SMELL SWEET FOR MANY MONTHS

Pluck a quantity of rose leaves and wipe them carefully. Place in a bowl and pound to a pulp. Add powdered orris root, a generous sprig of rosemary very well chopped, and a little tarragon.

Mix the ingredients well together, then place a little of the mixture in the palm of the hand and roll it into a 'bead' to the size you desire. Pierce it with a sharp pin and leaving the pin in place, set the bead on clean paper to dry.

Continue making beads until the mixture is all used up. When they are completely dry, remove the pins, varnish lightly, and thread on waxed cotton. As the necklace is worn, the heat of the body will bring out the perfume.

Orris is the finely ground powder of the iris. Mix a little wheat starch with it.

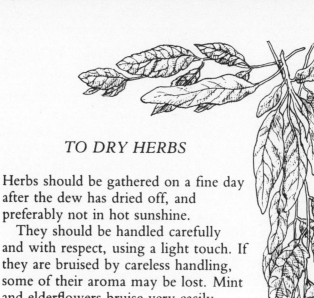

TO DRY HERBS

Herbs should be gathered on a fine day after the dew has dried off, and preferably not in hot sunshine.

They should be handled carefully and with respect, using a light touch. If they are bruised by careless handling, some of their aroma may be lost. Mint and elderflowers bruise very easily.

The best time to gather herb leaves is while the plant is still young, and before it starts to flower. The flowers of herbs should be picked while fully out.

To dry herbs, hang them, not too tightly bunched, in a well ventilated place such as a cupboard under the stairs, or lay them on racks or trays with a perforated base to allow the air to circulate. If they are packed too closely together they will go mouldy.

It is important that herbs are dried in darkness, for if they are exposed to the light, they will lose their green colouring.

TO EXTRACT PLANT OILS FOR CREAMS

Add leaves or flowers of the chosen plant to a mixture of one tablespoonful wine vinegar and half a pint olive oil. Pour into a bottle and stand for twenty-one days in sunlight, if possible. Give the bottle a vigorous shake-up at least twice a day.

After the twenty-one days, strain through fine muslin, making sure you squeeze all the oil from the residue of leaves or flowers. Pour the oil back into the bottle with a fresh supply of the herbs.

Repeat this process until the oil smells strongly of the chosen plant. You can dry and store flowers and leaves in advance if liked.

To add plant oil to cream, place the cream in a china bowl standing in water, or in the top part of a double saucepan. As the cream softens over gentle heat, stir in the oil, drop by drop, until the mixture is thoroughly scented with the herb.

SCENTED CREAMS

FOR A GOOD BASIC CREAM, place one part white wax, two parts lanolin, in a china bowl, in the upper part of a double saucepan over gentle heat. When softened beat well and add three parts almond oil.

A LAVENDER CREAM is unfailingly good, for lavender has virtues above all other for the skin. Put in an earthenware dish two ounces spermacetti, one ounce beeswax, five ounces almond oil.

Place the dish in a bowl of boiling water, and when the ingredients have melted, slowly add one dessertspoonful of pure lavender water, and a pinch of borax. Beat together very well, then put into china jars and screw down very tightly.

Oil of lavender can be used instead of the lavender water.

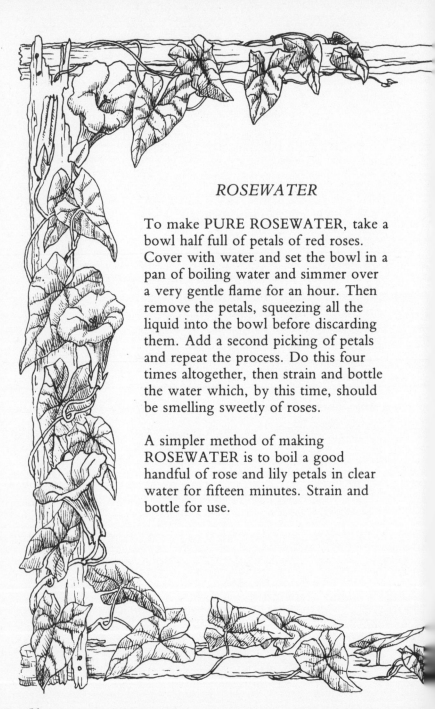

ROSEWATER

To make PURE ROSEWATER, take a
bowl half full of petals of red roses.
Cover with water and set the bowl in a
pan of boiling water and simmer over
a very gentle flame for an hour. Then
remove the petals, squeezing all the
liquid into the bowl before discarding
them. Add a second picking of petals
and repeat the process. Do this four
times altogether, then strain and bottle
the water which, by this time, should
be smelling sweetly of roses.

A simpler method of making
ROSEWATER is to boil a good
handful of rose and lily petals in clear
water for fifteen minutes. Strain and
bottle for use.

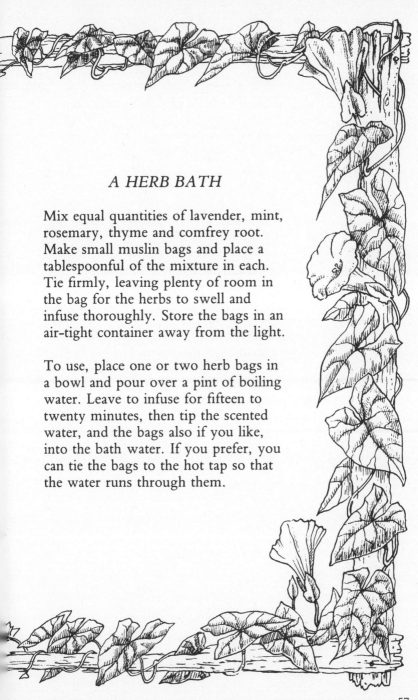

A HERB BATH

Mix equal quantities of lavender, mint,
rosemary, thyme and comfrey root.
Make small muslin bags and place a
tablespoonful of the mixture in each.
Tie firmly, leaving plenty of room in
the bag for the herbs to swell and
infuse thoroughly. Store the bags in an
air-tight container away from the light.

To use, place one or two herb bags in
a bowl and pour over a pint of boiling
water. Leave to infuse for fifteen to
twenty minutes, then tip the scented
water, and the bags also if you like,
into the bath water. If you prefer, you
can tie the bags to the hot tap so that
the water runs through them.

HERB PILLOWS

A SOPORIFIC PILLOW: mix a good
handful each of dried sage, lemon balm
and peppermint. Add a pinch of
verbena and a little crushed orris root
to fix the scents. Stuff a muslin bag
with the filling. Cover the pillow with
a pretty, flowery material.

Stuff dry BEECH LEAVES into a
pillow for sound sleep.

A pillowful stuffed with
THISTLEDOWN makes a beautiful,
soft headrest (and keeps the thistles
from spreading) but you will need to
collect a great quantity of down.
Gather it while it is fluffy and warmed
by the sun, and stuff it into a pillow
case, taking care not to gather any
sharp pieces of the plant as you do so.
You will find such a pillow softer than
any goosedown, and wonderfully cool
and sweet.

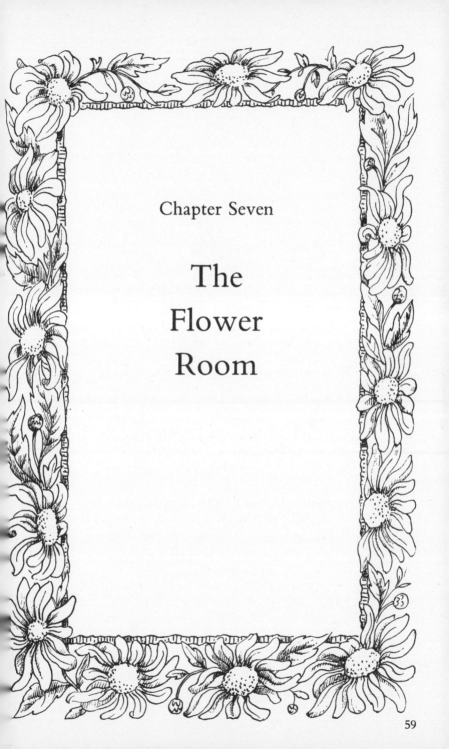

Chapter Seven

The
Flower
Room

TO PRESERVE A ROSEBUD
WHICH WILL LAST FOR
WEEKS

*Dip the rosebud in melted candle wax
letting it come halfway up the stem. Wave
the bud about to cool the wax. When the
wax is cool and firm enough to hold, dip
the other end of the stem in melted wax.*

*The wax coating will be very thin and
unnoticeable . . . and the bud will not fade.*

CARING FOR CUT FLOWERS

After cutting LILAC, peel the skin off the bark of the part of the stem that will be immersed in the water. This outer skin poisons the water. If the cut lilac droops, dip the stems in very hot, almost boiling water. Leave for about ten minutes and the flowers will revive.

POPPIES last longer if their stems are dipped in hot water, or held in the flame of a candle, before being put into the vase.

TULIPS do well with salt in the water. Never put them in a vase with other flowers.

ROSES last longer if their stems are slightly bruised before being put into the vase.

Never put a vase of flowers on a sunny windowsill.

Never stand a vase of flowers in a draught.

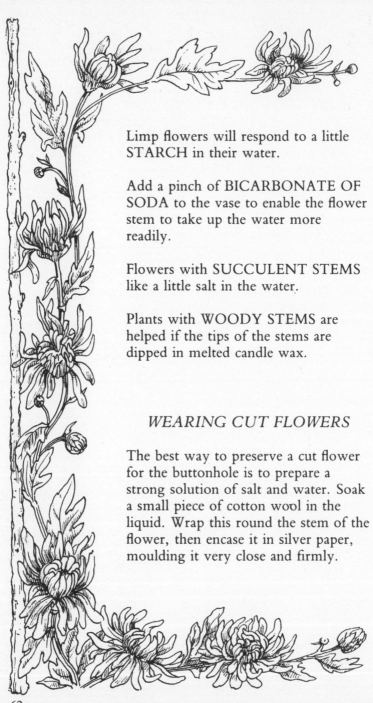

Limp flowers will respond to a little
STARCH in their water.

Add a pinch of BICARBONATE OF
SODA to the vase to enable the flower
stem to take up the water more
readily.

Flowers with SUCCULENT STEMS
like a little salt in the water.

Plants with WOODY STEMS are
helped if the tips of the stems are
dipped in melted candle wax.

WEARING CUT FLOWERS

The best way to preserve a cut flower
for the buttonhole is to prepare a
strong solution of salt and water. Soak
a small piece of cotton wool in the
liquid. Wrap this round the stem of the
flower, then encase it in silver paper,
moulding it very close and firmly.

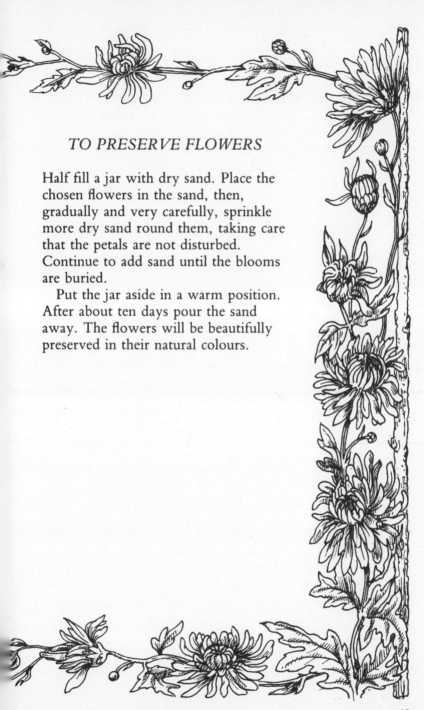

TO PRESERVE FLOWERS

Half fill a jar with dry sand. Place the chosen flowers in the sand, then, gradually and very carefully, sprinkle more dry sand round them, taking care that the petals are not disturbed. Continue to add sand until the blooms are buried.

Put the jar aside in a warm position. After about ten days pour the sand away. The flowers will be beautifully preserved in their natural colours.

Afterword

My Mother once told me that one of the great objects of a woman's life is to make herself attractive to everyone. "Beauty is only skin deep, you know," she said with a certain look in her eye. "To be really attractive requires more than a beautiful skin. It requires beautiful thoughts, too. For that which the mind dwells on will be revealed in the face" . . . a piece of information that made me think.

A woman calling herself 'Miss F.', writing about beauty in 1919, explained that rest is a great beautifier. We should all learn to relax whenever possible. "We must not only drop our bodies onto the bed when we take our rest. We must also drop our mental cares, and though it is not easy to do this, practice will make it easier, and the benefits derived from the habit will be manifold." This is as true now as it was in 1919, and just as difficult to do. . .

As a final word, I'll repeat the old saying that "Beauty is only skin deep" because I can't resist quoting the Frenchman who remarked, "And that's quite deep enough for me. . . ." Which brings me back to my Grandmother's recipes. I'm sure he would have approved of them.